Four hundred and sticking

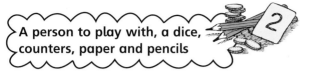

A person to play with, a dice, counters, paper and pencils

Take turns to throw the dice three times. Write down the numbers and use them to create a 3-digit number. For example, if you throw 3, 4 and 2, you could make 423.

When you have each had a turn, compare numbers. Whose is the closest to 400? That person takes a counter.

Continue playing until one person has ten counters. They win!

In class The children can play the game in pairs. Divide into two teams, tigers and lions. One child in each pair is a tiger and one is a lion. Add up the scores for each team.

Nine tens!

Place-value

Paper and pencils

Work out carefully how many numbers between 1 and 1000 have a '9' in the 'tens' place. Make notes to help you.

Is it the same as the number of numbers that have a '9' in the units place?

91, 92, 93, ...

191, 192, ...

19, 29, 39 ...

109, 119, ...

In class Discuss how to work this out. Use place-value cards to help.

Make up the ten

A person to play with, a dice and some counters

Throw the dice. Write down the number thrown. Show it to your partner.

They have to say the number that goes with that number to make ten. If they are correct, they can take that number of counters.

 6

4 goes with 6 to make 10.

Now they take a turn throwing the dice.
Keep playing until someone collects 30 counters!

In class Play as a class game. Children against teacher!

Edible money!

A person to talk to, some coins

Look in the kitchen. Choose something small which you like to eat.

Ask someone roughly how much it costs. (It needs to be between 20p and 90p.) Write down the amount.

Select the coins you would need to buy this. You need to choose the fewest coins possible.

Draw the food and label it. Then draw round the coins. Bring your drawing into school.

Organic Yoghurt 33p

In class Discuss all the different foods and the coins that the children chose. Perhaps display the children's drawings.

Along and across!

Paper and pencil

Use the first grid shown below as a model.

Add each pair of numbers vertically, and then add each pair of numbers horizontally.

Finally, add the totals, down and across. These should add up to the same number!

23	7	30
5	33	38

28   40   (68)

12	6
8	42

24	5
6	35

16	4
3	56

In class The children can design their own grid for a friend.

Daylight robbery!

A person to play with, some 10p coins

Each draw three purses on a page and write three amounts, one in each purse. Don't show the other person your purses.

Take turns to be the robber! Say the amount you are going to take. It has to be an amount between 1p and 6p.

The other person has to take that amount from one of their purses and write down the amount left.

Each do this three times. Show each other your pages. If any person has an amount left which ends in 1p, they win a 10p coin. Who gets most money? Play again.

In class Draw some purses and write some amounts on the board. Discuss how much the children will have to 'remove' to leave an amount in each purse that ends in 1p.

Which comes first?

Look at the number on each balloon. Write the number ten more and the number ten less.

Then write all the 3-digit numbers in order from smallest to largest. Which one comes first?

In class Write all the numbers in order on the board. Do the children's orders agree with yours?

Chancy business

A person to play with, some 10p coins, paper and pencils

Each write down a 3-digit number. It must not have a zero in it.

Take turns to spin a coin. If the coin lands heads, the person subtracts 100 from their number. If it lands tails, they add 100.

Whose number is closest to 500? That person takes a coin.

Play again. Have ten turns each. Who ends up with the most coins?

In class Play the game with the children, who work in pairs. Teacher against all of them!

4

Chocolates all round!

Paper and pencils, counters if needed

Look at each box of chocolates.

Some children are given two chocolates each from the boxes.

Write how many children can be given two chocolates from each box. For example, 10 children can have two chocolates from the first box.

> **In class** Write 23 on the board. How many children could have two chocolates each from this box? Discuss the answer (11).

Five pence Freddie

A person to play with, counters, paper and pencils

Each place a counter on a coloured square. The aim is to move your counter from the corner you start on to the opposite corner.

You may move one square at a time in any direction. No player may move their counter to a square occupied by another counter.

Each time you move onto a new square score that number of 5ps. For example, if you move on to '9', you score $9 \times 5p = 45p$.

	10	9	
6	4	3	8
7	9	5	1
	2	7	

When you are both on the opposite corner, add up the total amount you have scored. Who has the lowest score? They win!

> **In class** The children can play the game in pairs. Divide into two teams, tigers and lions. One child in each pair is a tiger and one is a lion. Add up the scores for each team.

Darts doubles

 Paper and pencils

Look at the picture of the dartboard.

Imagine you score the double of each number in turn.

Write down all your scores.

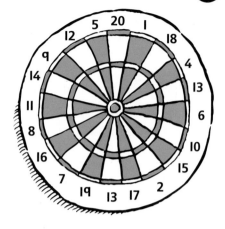

In class Draw a big dartboard and write in the doubles. Extend by working out the trebles.

Quarter for luck

A person to play with, a dice, some 2p and 10p coins, paper and pencils

Each take turns to throw the dice and write a 2-digit amount. For example, if you throw a 4 and a 3, you can write 34p.

Then try to halve that amount. If this can be done, take a 2p coin.

If you can split the amount into quarters, take two 2p coins.

Then the other person has a turn. Continue until one player has collected 20p or more (you can swap five 2p coins for a 10p coin).

In class Play the game with the children, working in pairs. Teacher against all of them!

Sum difference

Paper and pencils

Pair up each diamond with a circle and find the total (adding the two numbers) and the difference (taking the smaller number from the larger).

Do this for every possible pairing of the diamonds and circles.

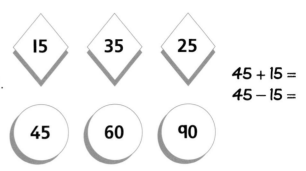

$45 + 15 =$
$45 - 15 =$

> **In class** Check to see that the children did find all the possible pairings. Demonstrate how to be sure we found them all!

Make 100

A person to play with, some coins

Cover each of the numbers on the grid with a coin.

Take turns to lift a coin. Look at the number beneath it.

Say the number that adds to this number to make 100. For example, if you lift a coin to reveal 35, you say 'sixty-five'.

The other person checks that you are correct. If so, you may keep the coin. If not, replace the coin.

When all the coins have been taken, who has the most money?

88	35	62	6
40	50	17	72
11	23	90	45

> **In class** Write pairs of numbers on balloons and hang these from the ceiling in the classroom!

Middle one out!

Paper and pencils

Write out these numbers, putting them in order from largest to smallest.

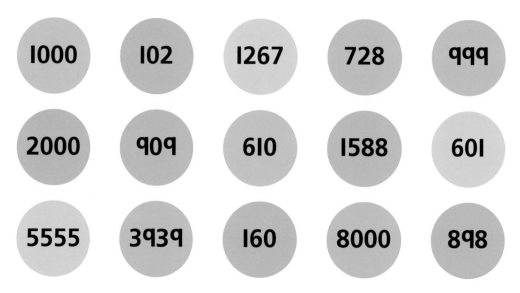

1000	102	1267	728	999
2000	909	610	1588	601
5555	3939	160	8000	898

Which number is in the middle? Think of something special about this number.

In class Discuss what is special about the middle number.

Up to one pound!

A person to talk to, some 10p coins, paper and pencils

Decide on three small things with prices below £1 that you would like to buy. Draw the items – they can be edible! Write their prices.

Write the amount you need to add to make the next 10p. Write the amount you need to add to make £1.

67p

In class Look at all the children's drawings and discuss the prices.
Which are expensive? Which are good value? Make a display of their drawings.

Make it cross!

Paper and pencils

Copy each of these crosses.

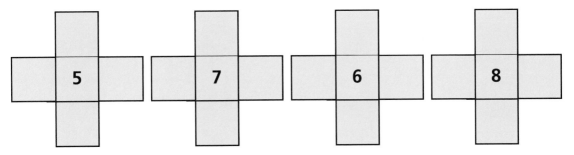

Write four numbers in the spaces, so that the difference between the top and the bottom number is the number in the middle, and the difference between the left-hand and the right-hand numbers is also the number in the middle.

BUT no two numbers in one cross can begin with the same digit. For example, in the first cross 36 and 41 would be correct, but 31 and 36 would not.

> **In class** Ask children to draw crosses for each other.

Toy reduction

A person to talk to, paper and pencils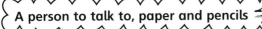

Talk to someone in your family about your favourite small toy or book. How much was it when it was bought? (It should be something that cost between £1 and £9.)

Draw your toy. Write down its price.

How much would it cost if the price were reduced by 20p?

Now, write down three other prices. Reduce each one of these by 20p and write the new prices.

> **In class** Discuss all the children's toys and make a display of all their drawings and the prices. Draw big 'Sale' signs and reduce all the prices!

Wall sums

Paper and pencils

62 – 31	98 – 66	57 – 24	79 – 45

46 –25	74 – 52	38 – 15	88 – 64	96 – 71

55 – 44	84 – 72	36 – 23	65 – 51	77 – 62	49 – 33

Copy the wall. But instead of writing the subtractions on each brick, write the answer.

At the end, without doing any subtractions, draw the next row of bricks and on top write numbers on them.

In class Draw another two layers of wall.

Tracking the sums

A person to play with, counters, paper and pencils

Use a counter each and place them on the start.

Take turns to spin a coin. Heads, move 2 spaces. Tails, move 1 space.

Each time you land, work out the answer to the addition. Check with your partner. If correct, score 10 points.

Keep playing until both of you reach the end of the track. Who has collected the most points?

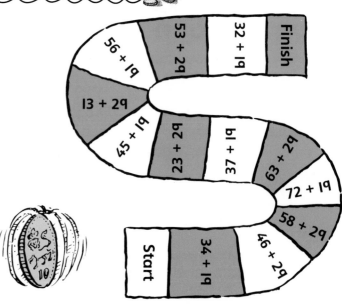

In class Play the game with the children, who work in pairs.

10

Fifty more

Paper and pencils

Look at each pile of 50p coins.

Count in fifties and work out how much there is in each pile.

Write the amount.

> **In class** Give a child a handful of 50p coins. How much do they have? Estimate, then count.

Even chances

Odd and even

A person to play with, one each of 50p, 20p, 10p, 5p, 2p and 1p coins, paper and pencils

Each decide whether you want to be even or odd. Take turns to play.

Spin each coin. Collect up those that land tails. Look at how much you have.

   **50p + 10p + 2p = 62p**

If the amount matches the type of number you collect (e.g. you are 'even'), then you score that amount. If not, you score nothing!

Let the next person have a go at spinning the coins. Keep playing until one person has scored over £2.

> **In class** Play the game with the children. Teacher against the class!

Pricey pair

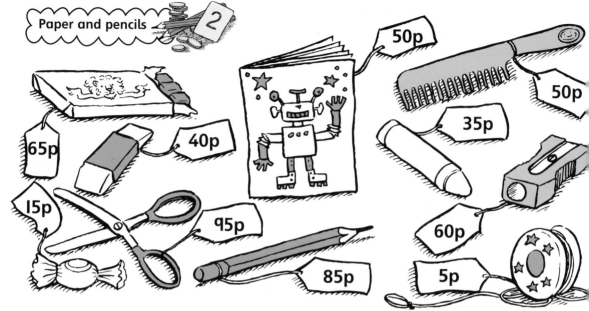

Paper and pencils

50p
50p
35p
65p
40p
15p
95p
60p
5p
85p

Look at all the prices.

Pair up all the items that would cost exactly £1 together and draw them.

In class Draw some items – the children have to price them so that pairs make £1.

Double or quit!

A person to play with, a dice, paper and pencils, some 2p coins

Take turns to throw the dice twice. Create a 2-digit number from the dice throws and write it down.

double 26 = 52

Each double your number and write the answer.

The person whose total is closest to 50 takes 2p. Play until someone has collected 30p.

In class Play the game. Teacher against all of the children!

Divide and rule

A person to play with, some dried beans or dry pasta pieces

Take turns to take a handful or two of beans.

Estimate how many beans there are. Count them carefully, grouping them in 5s and 10s.

Write the number. If it divides exactly by 2, score 2 points. If it divides exactly by 5, score 5 points. If it divides exactly by 10, score 10 points.

Now replace the beans and let the next person have a turn. Keep playing until one person has scored 25 points!

In class Play the game. Teacher against children!

Tables square

Paper and pencils

Copy the multiplication square and fill in the missing numbers.

×	3	6	10	4	5	1
5						
2			20			
1						
3						
4		24				
10						

In class Draw a large multiplication square on the board and fill it in together.

13

Three for all

A person to play with, counters of two colours

Take turns to choose a square on the grid and say the number.

Multiply that number by 3 and say the answer. If you are correct, place a counter on that square.

Both of you are trying to get three counters of your own colour in a line (horizontal, vertical or diagonal).

9	6	2	3	2	8
1	2	8	3	5	10
2	1	5	6	1	1
7	6	4	8	7	2
10	5	6	5	11	5
4	5	3	6	5	4

In class Play the game with the children, who work in pairs.

A fraction of the cost

Paper and pencils

Look at the jackets. How much would each jacket cost if it were $\frac{3}{4}$ of the price?
Look at the trousers. How much would each pair cost if it were $\frac{2}{3}$ of the price?
Write down all your answers.

In class Draw a piece of clothing on the board. Discuss how much it costs, roughly. Work out the cost if the price were halved!

Nearest hundred

A person to play with, some 10p coins, some home-made cards with 100, 200, 300, 400 ... 1000 written on them, paper and pencils

Each write down a 3-digit number. Show the number to the other person, who has to round it to the nearest hundred and write the answer.

Then take a card from the pile. Whose rounded total is nearest to the card number? That player takes a 10p coin.

Keep playing like this.

In class Play the game with the children, who work in pairs. Teacher against all of them!

Magic mixture!

Paper and pencils

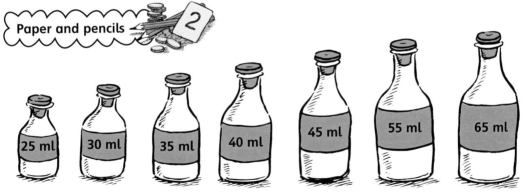

25 ml   30 ml   35 ml   40 ml   45 ml   55 ml   65 ml

Choose two bottles.

Work out how many ml of magic mixture you will have if you add them. Write down the addition.

Do this six times.

In class Draw three 'potion' bottles on the board. Encourage the children to combine all three and work out the total.

Take away track

A person to play with, a counter each, paper and pencils

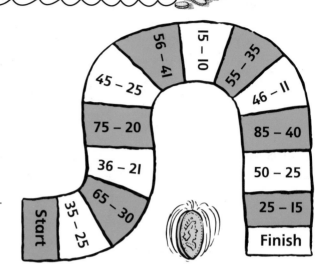

Each place a counter on start.

Take turns to spin a coin. Heads, move 2 spaces. Tails, move 1 space.

Each time you land, complete the subtraction shown. Check with your partner that it is correct. If it is, you may stay there. If not, move back 2 spaces.

Keep playing until one person reaches the end. They win!

In class The children can make up their own track game.

Saver's success

Paper and pencils

32p 26p 47p 51p 16p 24p 38p 45p 64p 58p 81p 78p

Look at each pair of children. Write the difference between the amounts they have saved.

Now look at all the children. Work out the difference between the one who has saved the most and the one who has saved the least.

In class Choose two children. They each say an amount. Work out the difference.

16

Three of a kind!

A person to play with, counters, some coins

25 14 35 23 45 12 65 23 75 20

Place counters on all the balloon numbers.

Take turns to remove three counters. Add the three numbers. Say the total. If it is correct, take a coin. Replace the counters.

The other person now removes three counters – but not the same three! They add the numbers.

Keep playing like this until someone has 10 coins.

> **In class** Draw circles on the board and place the same numbers in them.
> Cover with pieces of card held on with Blu-tack. Take turns to remove 3 pieces of card.

A bit more...

Paper and pencils

364	
	422
135	
	203
714	

20		200
	5	30
15		
		400
12		

$364 + 30 = 394$

Choose a number in the right-hand box.

Add it to one of the numbers in the left-hand box and write the addition.

Do this until you have written six additions, all correct!

> **In class** Draw the two boxes on the board. Choose some numbers and add them.

1000 and counting down

 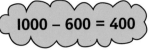

A person to play with, a dice, paper and pencils

Start with 1000.

The first person throws the dice. They subtract that number of hundreds and write the answer.

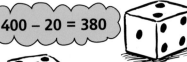

1000 – 600 = 400

The second person throws the dice. They subtract that many tens and write the answer.

400 – 20 = 380

The first person throws the dice. They subtract that many units and write the answer.

380 – 5 = 375

The second person throws the dice again. They subtract that number of hundreds and write the answer. If there are no hundreds left, move on to subtracting tens!

375 – 40 = 335

The first person to write a 1-digit number wins. Play again.

In class Play the game with the children. Teacher against the class!

Odds against us

Number patterns **N36**

Paper and pencils

Work out how many numbers there are between 10 and 100 where both digits are odd.

Try to use a system!

11, 13, 15

In class Discuss how the children were best to go about this.

Fishy frenzy!

A person to play with, paper and pencils

Choose a fish! Read the number. Multiply it by 100 and write the total.

Then let your partner have a turn.

After both of you have had three turns, add up all the numbers you have written down. Whose total is closest to 2000? They win! Play again.

> **In class** Draw some fish on the board and let the children play in pairs.

Stamp sticker

Paper and pencils

Choose the matching number of stamps for each parcel and write what they are. For example, the first parcel needs 2 × 10p and 1 × 5p.

Try to use the fewest stamps possible each time.

> **In class** Discuss the different ways of stamping some parcels, e.g. 180p = 6 × 30p or (3 × 50p) + 30p.

Four and against!

A person to play with, lots of counters, a coin

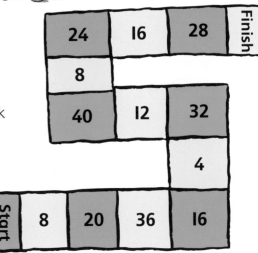

Each place a counter on start.

Take turns to spin a coin. Heads, move 2 spaces. Tails, move 1 space.

Each time you land, work out how many fours there are in the number shown. Check with your partner. If correct, you may take that many counters.

Keep playing until both of you reach the end. Who has the most counters? They win!

In class The children can invent their own tables track game!

Left overs

Paper and pencil

In each picture, some children are about to travel. The seats hold the number shown.

Answer these questions for each picture. How many seats will be full? How many children will be left over?

In class Present a similar problem about taking the class on a journey.

Button buddies

A person to play with, lots of counters

Place a counter over each button. Take turns to lift two counters. If the two fractions match, you may keep the two counters. If not, replace the counters.

Play until all the counters are taken. Who has most counters?

In class Write the same set of fractions on the board. Cover them with card and allow children to take off two cards. Are the fractions equivalent?

Animal sums!

Paper and pencil

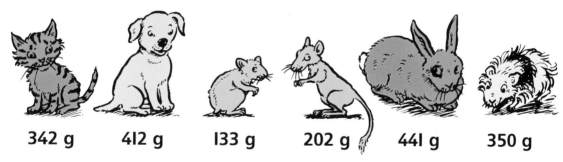

| 342 g | 412 g | 133 g | 202 g | 441 g | 350 g |

Choose two animals.

Work out their combined weight in grams. Add the two numbers in your head, then write the total and draw the animals.

Do this six times.

In class Look at which pairs the children chose. Choose some they didn't do.

Race the clock

A person to play with, a clock or watch, paper and pencil

Set a timer or put a piece of Blu-tack on the clock, so that you can time five minutes.

Choose one list each. Answer all the questions on your list.

After five minutes, check each other's work. Who has more correct?

465 + 357
276 + 354 + 138
What is four hundred more than 435?
Double 453
Add 255 to 366

362 + 49
194 + 353 + 117
What is five hundred more than 289?
Double 375
Add 199 to 211

In class The children can invent their own quiz.

How long?

A person to play with, a tape measure or ruler marked in cm

Choose a piece of furniture.

Each estimate how long you think it is in centimetres. Write down both your estimates.

Now use your ruler or tape measure to measure it. Write down the actual length. Draw the piece of furniture and bring all your estimates and measurements into school.

The sofa
Me: 175 cm
Mum: 250 cm
Actual length: 190 cm

In class Make a display of their drawings and discuss how close their estimates were!

Which of the three?

Paper and pencil

Look at each distance and decide which unit you would use to measure it.

Write kilometres, metres or centimetres for each one.

From bedroom to bathroom.	km	m	cm
From home to school.	km	m	cm
From bed to window.	km	m	cm
From front to back of book.	km	m	cm
From our town to New York.	km	m	cm
From nose to tail of dog.	km	m	cm
From front door to road.	km	m	cm
From fingertip to elbow.	km	m	cm

In class Discuss the units needed for each one. Discuss how the unit might differ from one child to another (e.g. it is metres from my home to the road, but kilometres from yours to the same road!).

The long and the short of it

A person to talk to, a newspaper with TV times in it

Start: 4.15
End: 4.35
Lasts: 20 minutes

Look in the newspaper at the page that tells you about TV and radio.

Choose your favourite TV or radio programme. Write down the start time. Write the time it ends.

Together, work out how long it lasts, and write this down.

Now do the same thing for your partner's favourite programme. Bring your work into school.

In class Make a graph of favourite programme lengths to the nearest 5 minutes.

Only five minutes!

Paper and pencil

Look at each clock. What's the time?

Write the time five minutes later.

In class Check the times with the children, and write the times another five minutes later.

Bathroom hunt!

A person to talk to, paper and pencils

Look in the bathroom. Can you find a container that is marked in ml?

Draw the container, label it and write the number of ml.

How many containers would you need to total more than a litre?

In class Make a display of their drawings and discuss the different things we measure in ml.

Hours of patience

Someone to work with, paper and pencil, calculator

Think about a baby or small child that you know.

Work out how many hours old they are.

Think about how many hours there are in a day, how many days in a month and how many months in a year.

Draw a picture of the baby and write the number of hours.

Laura
6, 480 hours

In class Make a display of their drawings and discuss how many hours we live each month!

Whose heavy purse?

Paper and pencils

900 g
475 g
75 g

50 g
600 g
500 g

350 g
$\frac{1}{2}$ kg
495 g

750 g
200 g
100 g

Choose two purses and add up how much they weigh together.

Pair up the purses so that each pair has a combined weight of 1 kilogram or less. Write all the pairs, e.g. 350 g + 600 g.

About how many kilograms would all the purses weigh together?

In class Discuss how much half a kilogram is. Discuss the pairs that add to 1000 g.

Months to go!

A person to work with, a calendar

Copy out the list of months.

Working together, think of something special that happens in each month. Write or draw it beside the month.

Bring your month list into school.

January
February
March
April
May
June
July
August
September
October
November
December

In class Make a display of their month lists. Chant the months in order.

Shape names

Paper and pencils

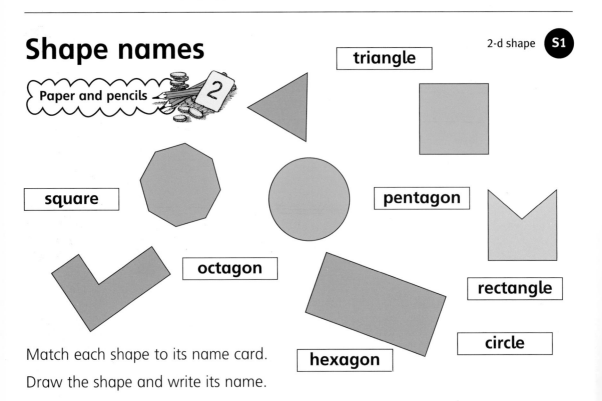

triangle

square

pentagon

octagon

rectangle

circle

hexagon

Match each shape to its name card.

Draw the shape and write its name.

In class Draw a shape on the board. The children have to say its name!

Symmetrical guesses

Someone to work with, scissors, paper and pencils

Fold a piece of paper down the middle.

One person draws half a shape against the fold line. The other person draws what they think the complete shape will look like.

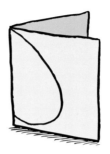
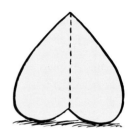

Then the first person cuts out their shape and opens up the paper. How close is the final shape to the drawing?

Repeat this process, swapping roles. Bring your shapes into school.

In class Draw a shape on the folded paper and ask the children to predict what the shape will be when it is cut and opened out.

Naughty elephants squirt water

Paper and pencils

N

Look at the map. Write the directions from:

The pond to the wood

The tractor to the haunted house

The shop to the church

The bridge to the church

The wood to the haunted house

The tractor to the graveyard

The graveyard to the church

The bridge to the pond

In class Discuss north, south, east and west, and how we remember these.

Prisms

Someone to work with, a piece of light card, scissors, sticky tape, pencils and crayons

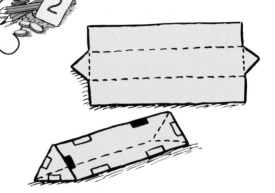

Copy the net shown here.

Cut it out round the thick black lines.

Fold it along the dotty lines.

Decorate the sides.

Stick it to make a prism.

In class Make a display of all the children's prisms by hanging them on thread from a line.

Table of shapes

Paper and pencils

Copy the table.

Fill in the number of edges, vertices and faces for each shape.

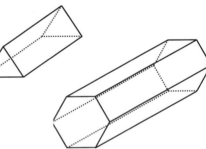

Shape	Edges	Vertices	Faces
Cuboid	12		
Triangular prism			
Triangle-based pyramid			
Cube			
Square-based pyramid			
Hexagonal prism			

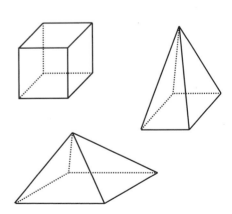

In class Draw the table on the board and complete it together.

Right on!

Someone to talk to, paper and pencils

Look around your home.
Find some examples of
right angles.

Write a list or draw
pictures of all the
examples you can find.

In class Discuss the different examples the children found.
Which ones were quite common? Which ones were quite unusual?

Twisting and turning

Paper and pencils

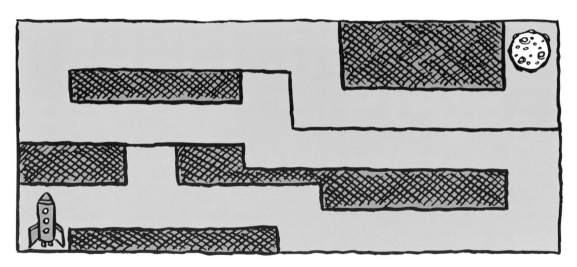

Using your finger, trace a route from the spaceship to the moon. Count the
number of turns you have to make to get there.

Check again, counting very carefully. Write down the number of turns.

In class Discuss the number of turns. Did the children agree?

Where are you?

Someone to play with and some coloured counters

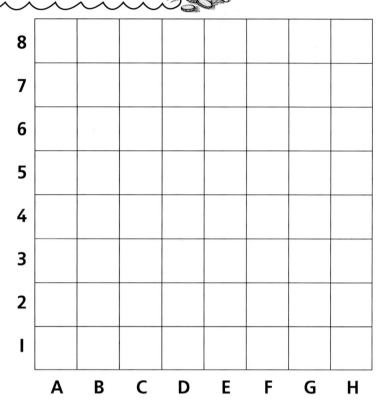

Take turns to place a counter on the grid. Before you position it, say the position – for example, 'I will put it on B5.'

The first person to place three of their counters in a row in any direction wins. The counters must touch.

In class Draw a grid on the board, and play. Children against the teacher!

Cutlery count-up

Tally charts D1

Paper, pencils and crayons

Copy the table and make a tally chart of the cutlery in your kitchen.

Cutlery	Tallies	Total
Knives		
Forks		
Teaspoons		
Pudding spoons		
Tablespoons		

In class Draw a large tally chart on the board. The children can all feed their data in.

Letter lottery

Someone to work with, paper, pencils and crayons

Write a list of all the names of the people in your home or who sometimes visit you.

Draw a frequency table to show many times the vowels appear in these names.

letter	frequency
a	
e	
i	
o	
u	

In class Draw a large frequency table on the board and allow the children to fill in all their data. Which letter comes out as most common?

Ice-cream count!

Bar graphs D3

Paper and pencils

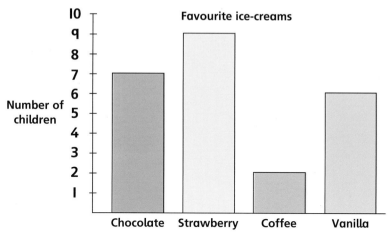

Look at the graph and answer these questions:
How many children liked strawberry?
How many liked chocolate?
Which ice-cream was the most popular?
Which was least popular?
How many more children liked vanilla than coffee?
How many children voted in all?

In class Discuss the graph. Which ice-creams do the children like?

TV pictograph

Paper and pencils

Survey your friends, neighbours and relations. Which sort of TV programme do they like best? Make a tally chart.

Copy the pictograph. Fill in the columns, taking care to use what you found out. Bring your finished graph into school.

Favourite TV programmes

								Key
comedy								
news								
wildlife								= 2 people
soap								
cartoon								

In class Discuss their graphs. Which types of programme were the most popular in general?